THE ROYAL HORTICULTURAL SOCIETY

BIRDWATCHER'S NOTEBOOK

F

FRANCES LINCOLN LIMITED
PUBLISHERS

Frances Lincoln Limited
4 Torriano Mews
Torriano Avenue
London NW5 2RZ
www.franceslincoln.com

The Royal Horticultural Society Birdwatcher's Notebook
Copyright © Frances Lincoln Ltd 2010
Text copyright © Frances Lincoln Ltd 2010
Photographs copyright © CJ WildBird Foods Ltd
Printed under licence granted by the Royal Horticultural
Society, Registered Charity number 222879/
SC038262. For more information visit our website or call
0845 130 4646. An interest in gardening is all you need
to enjoy being a member of the RHS.
Website: www.rhs.org.uk

First Frances Lincoln edition 2010

A catalogue record for this book is available from the
British Library

ISBN: 978-0-7112-3156-6
Printed in China
9 8 7 6 5 4 3 2 1

**Images throughout supplied by wildlife specialists
CJ WildBird Foods Ltd (www.birdfood.co.uk)**
Front cover: Goldfinch
Title page: Blue Tit (juvenile)
Opposite page: Starling (juvenile)

The publisher would like to thank CJ WildBird Foods Ltd for
contributing the photographs.

CJ WildBird Foods Ltd is a world leader in the research, development
and supply of wild bird and wildlife food, feeders and nesting
products. They have a wealth of in-house wildlife expertise and are
responsible for a significant number of developments in caring for
garden birds and wildlife, including the introduction of energy-rich
foods such as Sunflower Hearts and Nyjer Seed to the UK wild bird
market. In addition to foods, feeders, nest boxes and water baths
they advocate wildlife-friendly gardening and offer a range of plants,
bulbs, shrubs and trees specially selected to be most beneficial
for wildlife.

For more information please visit www.birdfood.co.uk or call their
customer service team on FREEPHONE 0800 731 2820 for helpful
advice.

If found please return to:

EQUIPMENT

Birdwatching can be one of the simplest of hobbies to pursue and need not cost a lot of money. All you need to get started are your eyes and ears, however, you also might find the following useful:

• Your *RHS Birdwatcher's Notebook* to record your observations. This will help hone your observational and identifying skills.

• Binoculars will enable you to see more details and thus improve your identifying skills. It is advisable to buy the best you can afford and if possible, try before you buy. Compact models are portable which is great, but if you have large hands you may find them too fiddly to use. If possible ask other birdwatchers what they use and do some research on the internet or in bird-watching magazines.

• Local field guide (*see* page 8).

• Avoid disturbing birds and their habitats and don't go too close. The bird's welfare is always the priority. Be particularly careful in the nesting season as disturbance can cause a bird to abandon its nest, which means the fledglings will most likely perish.

• Taking eggs from nests is illegal. Respect the various laws that are in place to protect birds and their habitats. The penalties for not doing so can be severe. If you are birdwatching abroad familiarize yourself with local birding regulations before your trip as laws will vary according to the country.

• If you do see a rare bird consider the impact on the wildlife and the countryside before making others aware of the location. Always inform the landowner, or warden if it is a nature reserve, before doing anything.

• Never put yourself at risk to get a better view of a bird. Your own safety should always be a priority.

Identify this bird .... (Answer p.144)

BIRDWATCHING TIPS

• You can increase the number and variety of birds that you see from your home by gardening in a wildlife-friendly manner and putting out good quality bird food, feeders and nest boxes. Adding a pond or well-placed bird bath will also attract birds and other wildlife.

• Study a field guide which is as specific to your local area as possible. Finding out more about the type of the bird you are likely to see locally will help you enormously. Time spent familiarizing yourself with colours and plumage of juveniles, males and females will pay dividends when you are in the field. If you are confident about the regular visitors you will be more likely to spot the rare ones. You can make notes on pages 114–121.

• Books with paintings are more accurate than photographs as lighting conditions can affect colours in photographs.

• A pocket guide is small enough to carry with you but do get into the habit of trying to identify the bird first and then look it up. This will improve your bird-spotting skills. You can start with trying to identify the birds in this book. All the names have been listed on page 144 but see if you can identify them before looking them up.

• Familiarize yourself with the names of different parts of the bird and the feather groups. This will make it easier to make field notes and sketches and will help when you are describing the bird to others (see page 11).

• Get to know the sizes of key birds along a scale from small to large. You can then compare other birds against your mental references. The size of birds in flight can be quite misleading so when doing comparisons make sure you are comparing like for like ie. both in flight or both at rest.

• Familiarize yourself with the description of common habitats (woodland, gardens, grassland, wetland etc). A brief note then will convey a large amount of information.

• Returning to one place regularly will help you build up a comprehensive picture of visitors at different seasons and different times of day, as well as changes in the appearance of the birds themselves.

• Do some advance research before visiting a new birding area so you know what birds you are likely to see and what they look like, as well as calls and behaviour. You can make notes on pages 114–121.

Identify this bird .... (Answer p.144)

• Birds are often heard before they are seen. Learning bird songs will give you a head start in identifying what is out there. There are many good recordings you can listen to.

• Spring and early summer are a good time to start birdwatching if you are a beginner as there is less confusion with winter visitors. Early morning and late afternoons are usually the best time of day. Ideally walk with the sun behind you as this will make it easier to see birds.

• When you are in the field always keep your binoculars ready around your neck so they are accessible when needed. When you sight your bird, try to keep your eyes on the bird and raise your binoculars to your eyes and only focus the binoculars once they are in position. This way you will keep the bird in your sights.

GETTING UP CLOSE

• Birdwatching relies on getting as close as possible to your subject. This will be easier if you consider your movements and what you are wearing. For example, certain fabrics make a noise when you move and may startle birds. Your movements should be slow and quiet. Bright colours will make you stand out rather than blend in with your surroundings. Ideally wear dull, leaf colours.

• If you are settling down to watch a particular spot, choose somewhere near shrubs and trees which will help you blend in. Make yourself comfortable and open any packets of food etc at the start so there won't be any sudden noises. Always clear up after yourself and leave nothing behind except your footprints.

• Many birdwatching sites have hides which are the perfect way to view birds. Respect other people using the hide and be quiet and unobtrusive.

LEARNING FROM OTHERS

• Join a local birdwatching group. This is a great way to learn from others as well as share what you know. There are also many annual national campaigns run by bird and nature organizations which rely on volunteers reporting back what they have seen.

• The internet offers a wealth of sites with invaluable birdwatching tips and advice from professionals and enthusiastic amateurs. See page 138.

• Birdwatching magazines are a good way of keeping in touch with the subject and learning more

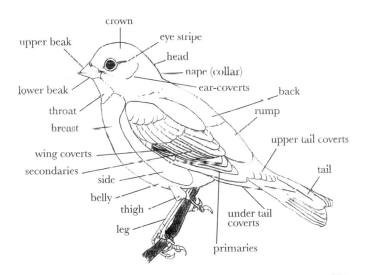

SKETCHING FOR REFERENCE

Ideally your field notes are a record of what you see and they can be a combination of written notes and pictures. Recording your sightings in this way will hone your powers of observation.

The idea of drawing what you see can seem a bit daunting but remember that your sketch is a reference drawing not a work of art. You do not need to include every detail of every feather! Concentrate on key areas of colour and details of the plumage. You might find it helpful to consider your sketch as a diagram rather than a drawing.

You can annotate parts of your drawing with notes about colour or distinctive characteristics.

SKETCHING TIPS:
- Practice copying photos or drawings of birds you are likely to see. Not only will this improve your drawing skills, but also you will quickly get a better sense of their shape and key characteristics, as well as learn what you should be looking out for.
- Set up feeding areas in a location where you can view and draw the birds comfortably. A regular food supply will encourage birds to visit and give them something to focus on so they stick around, giving you plenty of opportunities to draw them. If you can arrange this near a window it means you can pursue your hobby regardless of the weather.
- Try not to get bogged down in detail. Concentrate on capturing the gesture of the bird – what makes it identifiable – and its key characteristics.

- Visiting a zoo or aviary will also give you the chance to practise your drawing skills. But remember – the sketches in your notebook are about recording information, they are not meant to be works of art.
- You can always just draw a particular part of the body such as the head and beak or legs rather than draw the whole bird. Notice the shape of the beak, the shape and length of the tail and also of the legs and feet.

Identify this bird .... (Answer p.144)

FIELD NOTES

The notes you make out in the field are to help with identification. The more information you have about the environs and the specifics of the bird, the easier this will be. The very act of looking, noticing and writing down what you see will improve your observational skills.

It is helpful to record the location and a brief description of the habitat. Plus make a note of the bird's behaviour and any bird calls you can hear.

It is useful too to record the date and the weather. The weather affects what birds we are likely to see and when. You will then be able to look back and make year-on-year comparisons of sightings of particular visitors. You can summarize your findings in the Year Planners on pages 126–130.

Asking yourself key questions about size, shape and colour of birds you see will help you gather all the information you

Identify this bird .... (Answer p.144)

need. The following is a list of the type of questions you might want to consider.

PHYSICAL DESCRIPTION

What size is the bird? A good trick is to compare it to some well-known birds you are familiar with and then note whether the bird you are watching is larger or smaller.

What shape is the bird? Is it slim or stout? Although remember that birds can fluff up their feathers.

Is the bill/beak large, straight, pointed, curved, slender, heavy, flat, hooked, small or conical? What colour is the bill/beak?

Are the legs long or short? Long legs indicate that the bird is a wader. *Are the feet webbed? Can you see the colour of the legs and feet?*

How long is the tail? What shape is it? Is the tail short, forked, notched, square-tipped, round-tipped or pointed? How does the bird hold its tail – is it up or down? Can you see any regular tail movements?

Does the bird have a crest? If so, what is its shape and colour?

What is the predominant colour of the bird? Is it brightly coloured or of a sober hue?
What colour is the upper part (head, back, back wings and upper tail)?

What colour is the under part (throat, breast, belly and under the tail)?

Be as specific as you can about the positioning of colours and any bright patches.

Are there any conspicuous marks?

Is the bird spotted, streaked or striped?

Does the tail have any bands, spots or areas of white?

Is there a patch of colour on the rump?

Are the wings plain or do they have any bands of colour?

Are there any stripes or rings of colour around the eyes?

Are there any stripes or patches of colour on the crown?

Remember that lighting affects colour and juveniles may have different colour patterns to adults. Adult plumage may also change through the season.

SOUNDS

Is the bird making any sound? Describe its bird call by writing down the sound you hear phonetically.

BEHAVIOUR

What is the bird doing? If it is feeding, what is it eating?

Is it interacting with any other birds? If so, can you identify them?

Be as specific as you can in terms of describing the bird's behaviour.

LOCATION

Where is the bird? (in a tree, on the ground, in the water etc).

What is the habitat like?

Identify this bird .... (Answer p.144)

Date:	Time:
Name:	
Location:	
Habitat:	
Weather:	
Description:	

Date:	Time:
Name:	
Location:	
Habitat:	
Weather:	
Description:	

Date:	Time:
Name:	
Location:	
Habitat:	
Weather:	
Description:	

Date:	Time:
Name:	
Location:	
Habitat:	
Weather:	
Description:	

Identify this bird .... (Answer p.144)

Date:	Time:
Name:	
Location:	
Habitat:	
Weather:	
Description:	

Date:	Time:
Name:	
Location:	
Habitat:	
Weather:	
Description:	

Date:	Time:
Name:	
Location:	
Habitat:	
Weather:	
Description:	

Date:	Time:
Name:	
Location:	
Habitat:	
Weather:	
Description:	

Identify this bird .... (Answer p.144)

Date:	Time:
Name:	
Location:	
Habitat:	
Weather:	
Description:	

Date:	Time:
Name:	
Location:	
Habitat:	
Weather:	
Description:	

Date:	Time:
Name:	
Location:	
Habitat:	
Weather:	
Description:	

Date:	Time:
Name:	
Location:	
Habitat:	
Weather:	
Description:	

Date:	Time:
Name:	
Location:	
Habitat:	
Weather:	
Description:	

Identify this bird .... (Answer p.144)

Date:	Time:
Name:	
Location:	
Habitat:	
Weather:	
Description:	

Date:	Time:
Name:	
Location:	
Habitat:	
Weather:	
Description:	

Identify this bird .... (Answer p.144)

Date:	Time:
Name:	
Location:	
Habitat:	
Weather:	
Description:	

Date:	Time:
Name:	
Location:	
Habitat:	
Weather:	
Description:	

Identify this bird .... (Answer p.144)

Date:	Time:
Name:	
Location:	
Habitat:	
Weather:	
Description:	

Date:	Time:
Name:	
Location:	
Habitat:	
Weather:	
Description:	

Date:	Time:
Name:	
Location:	
Habitat:	
Weather:	
Description:	

Date:	Time:
Name:	
Location:	
Habitat:	
Weather:	
Description:	

Identify this bird .... (Answer p.144)

Date:	Time:
Name:	
Location:	
Habitat:	
Weather:	
Description:	

Date:	Time:
Name:	
Location:	
Habitat:	
Weather:	
Description:	

Date:	Time:
Name:	
Location:	
Habitat:	
Weather:	
Description:	

Date:	Time:
Name:	
Location:	
Habitat:	
Weather:	
Description:	

Identify this bird .... (Answer p.144)

Date:	Time:
Name:	
Location:	
Habitat:	
Weather:	
Description:	

Date:	Time:
Name:	
Location:	
Habitat:	
Weather:	
Description:	

Date:	Time:
Name:	
Location:	
Habitat:	
Weather:	
Description:	

Date:	Time:
Name:	
Location:	
Habitat:	
Weather:	
Description:	

Identify this bird .... (Answer p.144)

Date:	Time:
Name:	
Location:	
Habitat:	
Weather:	
Description:	

Date:	Time:
Name:	
Location:	
Habitat:	
Weather:	
Description:	

Date:	Time:
Name:	
Location:	
Habitat:	
Weather:	
Description:	

Date:	Time:
Name:	
Location:	
Habitat:	
Weather:	
Description:	

Identify this bird .... (Answer p.144)

Date:	Time:
Name:	
Location:	
Habitat:	
Weather:	
Description:	

Date:	Time:
Name:	
Location:	
Habitat:	
Weather:	
Description:	

Date:	Time:
Name:	
Location:	
Habitat:	
Weather:	
Description:	

Date:	Time:
Name:	
Location:	
Habitat:	
Weather:	
Description:	

Identify this bird .... (Answer p.144)

Date:	Time:
Name:	
Location:	
Habitat:	
Weather:	
Description:	

Date:	Time:
Name:	
Location:	
Habitat:	
Weather:	
Description:	

Date:	Time:
Name:	
Location:	
Habitat:	
Weather:	
Description:	

Date:	Time:
Name:	
Location:	
Habitat:	
Weather:	
Description:	

Identify this bird .... (Answer p.144)

Date:	Time:
Name:	
Location:	
Habitat:	
Weather:	
Description:	

Date:	Time:
Name:	
Location:	
Habitat:	
Weather:	
Description:	

Date:	Time:
Name:	
Location:	
Habitat:	
Weather:	
Description:	

Identify this bird .... (Answer p.144)

Date:	Time:
Name:	
Location:	
Habitat:	
Weather:	
Description:	

Date:	Time:
Name:	
Location:	
Habitat:	
Weather:	
Description:	

CHECKLIST OF BIRDS LIKELY TO SEE

Becoming familiar with birds you are likely to see in your local area or at a particular location will improve your observational skills. Write a list of them here, together with the location and, if you like, add in key characteristics to jog your memory. This is particularly useful to do if you are visiting an unfamiliar location on a birding trip.

Identify this bird . ... (Answer p.144)

Identify this bird .... (Answer p.144)

BIRDS SEEN

Date:	Name:	Location:

Date:	Name:	Location:

Date:	Name:	Location:

Date:	Name:	Location:

Identify this bird .... (Answer p.144)

YEAR PLANNER

YEAR:	201 ...
JANUARY	JULY
FEBRUARY	AUGUST
MARCH	SEPTEMBER
APRIL	OCTOBER
MAY	NOVEMBER
JUNE	DECEMBER

YEAR:	201 ...
JANUARY	JULY
FEBRUARY	AUGUST
MARCH	SEPTEMBER
APRIL	OCTOBER
MAY	NOVEMBER
JUNE	DECEMBER

JANUARY	JULY

FEBRUARY	AUGUST

MARCH	SEPTEMBER

APRIL	OCTOBER

MAY	NOVEMBER

JUNE	DECEMBER

YEAR:	201...
JANUARY	JULY
FEBRUARY	AUGUST
MARCH	SEPTEMBER
APRIL	OCTOBER
MAY	NOVEMBER
JUNE	DECEMBER

YEAR:	201...
JANUARY	JULY
FEBRUARY	AUGUST
MARCH	SEPTEMBER
APRIL	OCTOBER
MAY	NOVEMBER
JUNE	DECEMBER

Identify this bird .... (Answer p.144)

Identify this bird .... (Answer p.144)

Identify this bird .... (Answer p.144)

USEFUL WEBSITES

There is a wealth of information available on the internet. Here is a small selection of sites you may find useful.

Wild About Gardens
Joint website by the RHS and The Wildlife Trust encouraging birds and other wildlife into your garden.
www.wildaboutgardens.org

The Royal Society for the Protection of Birds
The RSPB is the UK charity working to secure a healthy environment for birds and all wildlife. It has an excellent interactive bird identifier supported by coloured drawings, bird song and video footage.
www.rspb.org.uk

RSPB bird guide
Easy, automated bird identification tool for UK birds from the RSPB.
www.rspb.org.uk/wildlife

British Trust for Ornithology
The British Trust for Ornithology's volunteer surveyors and members work in partnership with BTO scientists to provide unbiased information about birds and their habitats.
www.bto.org/gbw

Birds of Britain
Monthly web magazine for birdwatchers.
www.birdsofbritain.co.uk

Bird Guides
Offers up-to-the-minute news and views on British and Irish birds, comprehensive online and mobile reference, a huge photo library and the products for birdwatchers everywhere.
www.birdguides.com

Birdwatch
Independent magazine established in 1992 offering an online home for birding.
www.birdwatch.co.uk

The Wildfowl & Wetlands Trust
The Wildfowl & Wetlands Trust (WWT) is a leading conservation organisation saving wetlands for wildlife and people across the world.
www.wwt.org.uk

Birding UK
The Birding UK and Ireland Community was set up to help people who are interested in birds whether they are experienced birders or absolute beginners.
www.birding.uk.com

Wild About Britain Forums
British wildlife and environment forums
www.wildaboutbritain.co.uk/forums

World Birds
Steve Oakes' inspirational website with pictures, an interactive map showing good birding sites and more.
www.world-birds.co.uk

British Garden Birds
British Garden Birds is dedicated to helping garden birdwatchers to identify and enjoy the birds that visit their gardens, and to understand the birds' lives and behaviour.
www.garden-birds.co.uk

CJ WildBird Foods Ltd
CJ WildBird Foods Ltd is a world leader in the research, development and supply of wild bird and wildlife food, feeders and nesting products.
www.birdfood.co.uk

INTERNATIONAL WEBSITES

Fatbirder
Fatbirder is an international online resource about birds, birding
and birdwatching for birders.
www.fatbirder.com

American Birding Association
www.aba.org

American Bird Guide
Information for birdwatching and birding from American
Bird Guide.
www.americanbirdguide.com

American Bird Center
Promoting the understanding, conservation and enjoyment
of North American birds.
www.americanbirdcenter.com

Birding.com
Birdwatching In the USA and around the world.
www.birding.com

Cornell Lab of Ornithology
Home to the world's largest collection of birdsong.
www.birds.cornell.edu

BirdSource
America's national database of bird sighting information.
www.birdsource.org

eNature.com
The National Audubon Society Field Guides
www.enature.com

Wildbirds.com
North American site focusing on birding around your yard
and around the world. Aimed at beginners and backyard
birdwatchers.
www.wildbirds.com

Birdwatching Australia
A directory of Australian birdwatching tours, bird clubs, freelance-guides, bird-orientated accommodation and reference information.
www.ausbird.com

New Zealand Birds
New Zealand birding sites.
www.nzbirds.com

The National Wetland Trust of New Zealand
www.wetlandtrust.org.nz

CONTACTS

Name
Address

Telephone
Mobile
E-mail

Name
Address

Telephone
Mobile
E-mail

Name
Address

Telephone
Mobile
E-mail

Name
Address

Telephone
Mobile
E-mail

Identify this bird .... (Answer p.144)

Name
Address

Telephone
Mobile
E-mail

Name
Address

Telephone
Mobile
E-mail

Name
Address

Telephone
Mobile
E-mail

CONTACTS

Name

Address

Telephone

Mobile

E-mail

Name

Address

Telephone

Mobile

E-mail

KEY TO ILLUSTRATIONS

Page 6: Coal Tit **Page 9:** Reed Bunting (male) **Page 13:** Blue Tit
Page 14: Long-tailed Tit **Page 17:** Tree Sparrow **Pages 18–19:**
Blue Tit feeding juvenile **Page 27:** Blue Tit (juvenile) **Page 35:**
Kingfisher **Page 45:** Chaffinch (male) **Page 49:** Wren **Page 53:**
Nuthatch **Page 61:** Reed Warbler feeding young **Page 69:** Robin
Page 77: Pied Wagtail **Page 85:** Chaffinch (juvenile) **Page 93:**
Nuthatch **Page 101:** Waxwing **Page 107:** Chaffinch (male)
Pages 112–113: Goldfinch **Page 117:** Greenfinch **Page 121:**
Great Tit **Page 125:** Greenfinch **Page 131:** Blackbird nestlings
Page 133: Mistle Thrush **Page 136:** Meadow Pipit **Page 143:** Robin